Give Me a Home Among the Gum Trees

Written by **Bob Brown & Wally Johnson**

Illustrated by **Ben Wood**

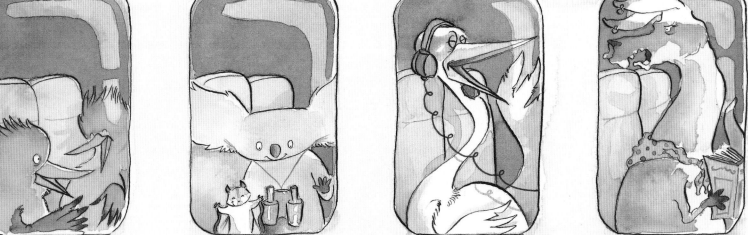

An Omnibus Book from Scholastic Australia

Dedicated to Wally Johnson,

who left us far too early — B.B.

For Mum and Dad, and for Geoff,

Paul, Albert and Roland — B.W.

Omnibus Books
175–177 Young Street, Parkside SA 5063
an imprint of Scholastic Australia Pty Ltd (ABN 11 000 614 577)
PO Box 579, Gosford NSW 2250.
www.scholastic.com.au

Part of the Scholastic Group
Sydney • Auckland • New York • Toronto • London • Mexico City •
New Delhi • Hong Kong • Buenos Aires • Puerto Rico

First published in 2008.
Reprinted in 2008, 2009.
First published in this edition in 2011.
Reprinted in 2011, 2012, 2013, 2014, 2015.
Text copyright © Mushroom Music Pty Ltd, 2008.
Illustrations copyright © Ben Wood, 2008.

National Library of Australia Cataloguing-in-Publication entry

Brown, B. (Robert Alexander).
Give me a home among the gum trees.

ISBN 978 1 86291 892 4 (pbk.).

1. Australia – Songs and music – Juvenile literature. I. Johnson, Wally.
II. Wood, Ben. III. Title.

782.4215990269

Typeset in GarthGraphic.
Scans by Graphic Print Group, Adelaide.
Printed and bound by TWP Sdn. Bhd.

10 9 8   16 17 18 19 20 / 0

I've been around the world a couple of times
or maybe more

I've seen the sights

and had delights

on every foreign shore

But when my friends all ask me 'bout the place that I adore
I tell them right away

Give me a home among the gum trees
With lots of plum trees

A sheep or two

A kangaroo

A clothesline out the back

Verandah out the front
And an old rocking chair

You'll see me in the kitchen
Cooking up a roast

Or Vegemite on toast

Just you and me

And a cup of tea

And later on we'll settle down
Beside the hitching post
And watch the possums play.

Give me a home among the gum trees
With lots of plum trees
A sheep or two
A kangaroo
A clothesline out the back
Verandah out the front
And an old rocking chair